Mike **KALUTA**
artist

Lovern **KINDZIERSKI**
color artist

Original Edition Art Assistance from:
Phil Trumbo, Mike Cody, Steve Hickman,
Berni Wrightson, Howard Chaykin

Berni Wrightson
Inker, "The Kingdom of the Cobra"

Len Wein
Co-author, "Death Is Bliss"

"IN THE TOILS OF WING FAT"

Mike Kaluta
writer/artist

Todd Klein
letterer

Elaine Lee
colorist

Color Art Assistance:
Pamela Johnson and Chris Chuckry

THE PRIVATE FILES OF THE SHADOW

Published by DC Comics Inc., 666 Fifth Avenue, New York, NY 10103,
under license from Condé Nast Publications Inc. The stories, characters,
and incidents in this book are entirely fictional. All characters featured
in this publication and their distinctive likenesses are trademarks of
Condé Nast Publications Inc. This collection copyright © 1989 Condé
Nast Publications Inc. Originally published in magazine form as
The Shadow #1–4 and #6, 1973–74.

Cover painting by Mike Kaluta
Publication design by Janice Walker

JENETTE KAHN
President & Publisher

DICK GIORDANO
V.P.–Executive Editor

RICHARD BRUNING & MARK WAID
Co-editors, collected edition

TERRI CUNNINGHAM
Managing Editor

PAT BASTIENNE
Mgr.–Talent Relations

BOB ROZAKIS
Production Director

PAUL LEVITZ
Executive V.P.

JOE ORLANDO
V.P.–Creative Director

BRUCE BRISTOW
V.P.–Sales & Marketing

TOM BALLOU
Advertising Director

MATT RAGONE
Circulation Director

PAT CALDON
Controller

Into the Shadow

BY DENNIS O'NEIL

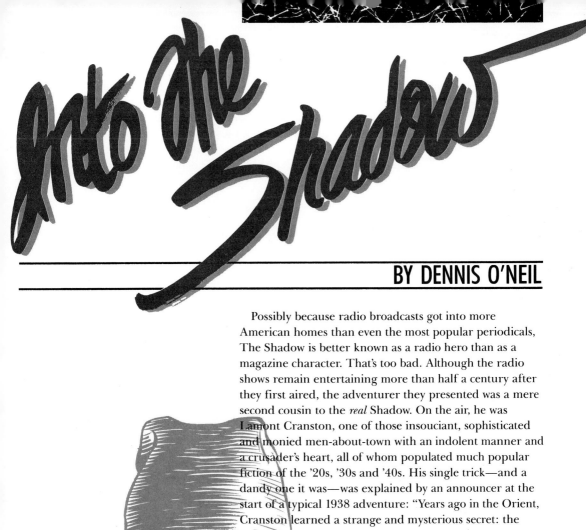

Possibly because radio broadcasts got into more American homes than even the most popular periodicals, The Shadow is better known as a radio hero than as a magazine character. That's too bad. Although the radio shows remain entertaining more than half a century after they first aired, the adventurer they presented was a mere second cousin to the *real* Shadow. On the air, he was Lamont Cranston, one of those insouciant, sophisticated and monied men-about-town with an indolent manner and a crusader's heart, all of whom populated much popular fiction of the '20s, '30s and '40s. His single trick—and a dandy one it was—was explained by an announcer at the start of a typical 1938 adventure: "Years ago in the Orient, Cranston learned a strange and mysterious secret: the hypnotic power to cloud men's minds so they cannot see him." Now, invisibility is terrific for a radio hero; after all, radio *is* disembodied voices. But it's a pretty passive skill—not really too exciting, this business of causing one's enemies *not* to do something.

The pulp Shadow—the one Shadow aficionados consider the genuine article—never became invisible. He *did* often use a black cape and slouch hat to melt into the darkness, but if some foolish villain turned on the light, there he would be, and woe to the bad guy. As Jim Steranko observed, the Shadow didn't believe in the death penalty . . . he *was* the death penalty. A pair of .45 caliber automatic pistols were among the foremost tools of his trade, and while he was no Ramboesque slaughterer, when he shot, he shot to kill. He had other tools, too: fast cars, a prototypical helicopter called an autogyro, airplanes, a girasol ring with which he hypnotized people (not to cloud their minds but, usually, to obtain information).

**A**nd he had helpers, a whole gang of them: on radio, he was aided only by his "friend and companion, the lovely Margo Lane" and a comic-relief cab driver named Shrevvy; in print, he had dozens of assistants from whom he demanded and got total and unthinking loyalty. Finally, the pulp Shadow was not Lamont Cranston; Cranston was a rich guy whose identity the Shadow sometimes borrowed. The Shadow was really Kent Allard, a World War I aviator.

The Shadow novels—there are 325 of them—began appearing monthly on newsstands in April of 1931. Most were written by the extraordinary Walter Gibson, a magician, journalist, feature writer, and novelist who could type up to 15,000 words of sturdy, readable narrative a day in an era that predated electric typewriters, much less computers. Gibson's relentless productivity makes every other prolific writer I've ever met seem like a pale, trembling aesthete by comparison; he once said that he sometimes had to stop working when his fingertips became bloody. When *The Shadow Magazine*'s publisher, Street and Smith, decided to bring Gibson's character to the then-new medium of comic books, Gibson wrote those, too.

In 1949, *The Shadow Magazine* ceased publication and five years later the radio show was cancelled. But The Shadow was not forgotten. In 1964, Radio Comics revived him in a version that gives purists the cringes: *this* Shadow was costumed in bright colors and used such silly gimmicks as springs in his boot soles to facilitate high jumps; to call him a travesty would be to honor him. After (a mercifully few) eight issues, he vanished, and The Shadow re-entered limbo.

In 1973, someone at DC Comics—possibly Carmine Infantino, who was editorial director at the time—decided The Shadow was again revivable. I was under contract as a freelance writer-editor for the company, and, probably because I had written Batman, The Shadow's heir apparent, Carmine chose me to bring The Shadow to the DC universe. There were a number of immediate decisions to be made. The first was: should we modernize him? I said no. It seemed to me at the time that there was no point in doing the character unless we could do him as Walter Gibson had conceived him back in 1931; if we were going to cobble together just another super-doer, we might as well not use The Shadow's name and save royalty payments to Street and Smith's successor, Condé Nast Publications, and if we planned to be faithful to Gibson's vision, we *had* to set the stories in an earlier era—we couldn't have a lethal vigilante with his own private army marauding around modern New York saving the taxpayers court costs without offending a lot of sensibilities, including mine. But even then, 15 years ago, the '30s were receding into folklore, becoming tinged with the never-never qualities of the

Old West. Nobody expected Wyatt Earp to read the Clantons their rights before dropping them into the dust of the OK Corral, and I was reasonably certain that nobody would mind if an historical Shadow forewent the amenities of due process, either. The second necessary decision was a bit more subtle: how should we handle The Shadow's characterization? Should we make him a humanitarian fighting for the American Way? A friendly father-figure doing only what he had to do? Should we show him relaxing after a hard night with a cold lemonade and a warm fire? Again, the answers had to be no. The Shadow worked best, I judged, as something akin to a force of nature. Readers had to accept as a given that he was always right, at least about what was evil and what was not. He killed because he *knew*, to an absolute certainty, that his enemies deserved death. Which created a problem. Human beings, even fictional ones, are not capable of such godlike insight if they are to be believable. So we were not permitted to know The Shadow's thoughts, nor his motivations, nor his background. He *was*, period. Of course, reading about moral abstractions tends to be pretty chilly entertainment, but I had Margo, Harry, and the rest of the crew to carry the human interest elements of the stories. And, by conferring on the Shadow the cachet of a demigod, I was able to redeem his helpers from being mindless cult-followers. Unthinking obedience to a man is fascism; unthinking obedience to a deity is merely good sense. None of this was original with me; it was all at least powerfully implicit in Gibson's novels.

Our comic book Shadow survived for 12 issues. (Issues 1–4 and 6, reprinted in this book, were illustrated by Mike Kaluta, with assistance from Berni Wrightson and other friends of Mike's; issues 5 and 7–9 were drawn by Frank Robbins; and the final three were rendered by E.R. Cruz.) I had no reason to doubt that *The Shadow* was a success. Then, suddenly, the series was cancelled. I was not told why—I first learned of the cancellation when a reader pointed out that *The Shadow* had been omitted from the company's subscription ad—but that was not unusual; in those relatively benighted days, comic-book editors were seldom made privy to decisions that affected their professional lives. I lamented the end of what had been a different and rewarding assignment—very likely, I grumbled aloud a bit—and went to earn my bread elsewhere.

The Shadow again retired to hero's limbo.

But he wasn't forgotten. His popularity may be minor, but it is very enduring. I'm not sure why, exactly. I've toyed with the idea that he conforms to some archetype, some common idea or image that is adapted, usually unconsciously, by individual storytellers to fit their needs. I've probed my memory, that of colleagues, and an odd reference book or two, searching for a mythological predecessor. They aren't hard to find for most super-heroes: Superman is a recasting of Gilgamesh and Moses,

among others; The Flash is a modern Apollo; Hawkman and
Hawkwoman are Daedalus and Icarus; even Spider-Man—
squint hard at him and you might glimpse the animal trickster
figures of Native Americans. But The Shadow? Well, he
certainly has his own descendants: in the pulps, there were
The Spider, The Bat and The Black Bat; on radio, The Green
Hornet; and in comics, a small army of masked vigilantes—The
Black Terror, the Crimson Avenger, The Hangman, Dr. Mid-
Nite, The Sandman, and a dozen more, including, of course,
The Batman. All probably owe some debt of inspiration to
The Shadow. But what inspired *him*? What was boiling in Walter
Gibson's subconscious when he sat down to write *The Shadow
Strikes*, the first Shadow tale? Maybe nothing—at least, nothing
from mythology, religion or folklore. Gibson acknowledged a
debt to Frank L. Packard, author of the Gray Seal stories, and it's
likely he was influenced by Poe and Doyle. But his predecessors
emphasized ratiocination, detection, adventure. Those elements
are present in Gibson's work, abundantly, but they're not what it's
about: what it's about is making civilization safe for civilized
people, reclaiming urban centers from the lawless. Maybe Walter
Gibson's genius was to *create* instant folklore by embracing urban
anxiety—by presenting a personification of that anxiety as good
instead of bad. As Chris Steinbrunner perceptively wrote,
"Menacing figures dressed in black had long been popular
characters in mystery stories, films, and plays . . . Gibson took
this terrible, dread shape that had hitherto been the hero's
nemesis and made it the hero. The Shadow was both the force
for good and lurker in the darkness."

Gibson's work appeared in the logical place for it: the pulps,
magazines printed on the cheapest paper and generally devoted
to the sensational—the venue of blue-collar literature, of stories
intended for working people, the post-Industrial Revolution
equivalent of the campfire. No pretensions here, not much to
interest the literary establishment, which pays no attention to
folklore until it has been dead and calcified long enough to be
classified and categorized and thus rendered safe for study. No,
Gibson was doing what storytellers have always done, taking the
hopes and aspirations and fears—especially the fears—of his
audience and magnifying them, embellishing and purifying
them and giving them form.

Consider: the cities had changed from havens against hostile
nature, places where everyone could aspire to enjoy the benefits
of civilization, and had become dark, treacherous warrens full of
terror. Opulent gangsters with tommyguns ruled from penthouses, dirty little thugs with revolvers lurked in the alleyways,
men driven by frustration and poverty prowled ghettos preparing to prey on their fellows. Or so it must have seemed to the
working stiff, afraid for himself and his family, terrified of what
was waiting on the cold pavements outside his living room, when

he plunked down his quarter for an evening's reading. The hero proper for such an era and place had to be himself at home in those penthouses, alleyways, and ghettos. He had to be as tough, as ruthless, as unforgiving as any villain. But, being a hero, he had to be on the side of justice. Not of the Establishment: our working stiff knew in his bones that the Establishment was corrupt. But justice, yes. In Raymond Chandler's unforgettable words, "Down these mean streets a man must go who is not himself mean, who is neither tarnished nor afraid." There were the private eyes for readers with a taste for realism, or what masqueraded as realism; for those who liked the extravagant, the romantic, the wildly melodramatic—those who wanted their heroes to be the stuff of legends—there was The Shadow.

His radio show is seldom aired, and he has never been on television. His magazines are decades old. Nobody but stone pop culture freaks ever sees the five Shadow movies made in the '30s and '40s (which is too bad: the one I've seen, a serial starring Victor Jory, is pretty good). Even as a comic book hero, he has always had limited longevity. But he lives. Today, he may call himself The Executioner, The Destroyer, The Equalizer, Mike Hammer, Batman. But he is, always, in some measure, The Shadow. Occasionally, he even reappears as himself, as he does in this volume, and in the (yet again) revived comics series DC currently publishes. I'm certain he will continue to reappear from time to time, here and there. It's always refreshing to look at the original.

Meanwhile, he's in the book you hold, as faithful an homage to Walter Gibson's populist genius as Mike Kaluta and I could manage. Read the stories, enjoy them, pretend for a moment that there really is a black-clad personage haunting the cold pavements who will keep the terrors in check. That's a healthy kind of pretense, the kind a working stiff needs if he's to get a good night's sleep now and then.

Dennis O'Neil
Halloween, 1988

The Shadow

HE IS FEARED BY ALL WHO TRANSGRESS THE LAW, BY ALL WHO PLAN EVIL...HE COMES FROM NOWHERE AND MELTS BACK INTO NOTHINGNESS AS SILENTLY AS HIS NAMESAKE...

HE ACTS IN THE NAME OF JUSTICE, STRIKING SWIFTLY, STUNNINGLY, FINALLY...

WITH SPITTING AUTOMATICS AND A LAUGH THAT CHILLS THE MARROW, HE LEADS A BAND OF LOYAL AGENTS AGAINST THE NATION'S WRONGDOERS....

THE DOOM PUZZLE

FOLLOW HIM NOW, AS HE BATTLES THE CLOCK IN A DESPERATE RACE TO SOLVE...

12

HERE, ON THE BROOKLYN WATER-FRONT THIS DANK NIGHT, THE AIR IS AS COLD AS THE FINGERS OF THE DEAD...

...IN THE DISTANCE, A FOGHORN MOANS--OR IS IT THE CRY OF SOME-THING LOST, SOMETHING DAMNED?

THE SEA LAPS AGAINST THE PIERS...

...OTHERWISE, ALL IS DARK, EXCEPT FOR A SINGLE, LIGHTED WINDOW IN AN ANCIENT WAREHOUSE...

...FROM BEHIND THE YELLOW-GLOWING GLASS THERE IS THE DRONE OF HARSH VOICES, HEARD BY A SOLITARY CLOAKED LISTENER...

SO GIMME THE DOUGH, OR YOU AIN'T EVEN GONNA SEE THE INFO!

I OUGHTTA GIVE YOU AN EYEFUL OF LEAD, SLOB! BUT TAKE YOUR STINKIN' MONEY...

...AN' DELIVER--

HUH--? WHAT'S THAT?

HA HA HA HA

THAT LAUGH--! IT'S LIKE... ICE!

ONLY ONE GUY'S GOT A LAUGH LIKE THAT-- AN' IT CAN'T BE... HIM!

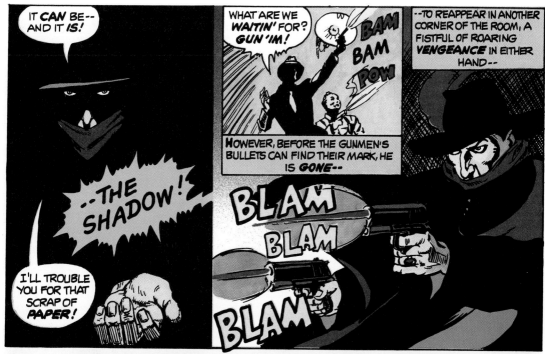

OUTSIDE, HE EMERGES FROM THE FOG AND GLIDES INTO A WAITING TAXI...

I HEARD *SHOTS!* ANY *TROUBLE,* BOSS?

JUST THE *USUAL,* SHREVVY!

DID YOU GET WHAT YOU *CAME* FOR?

YES, MARGO, I DID! -- THIS *MESSAGE!*

To all concerned: Flag and gun alike should arrive on land, water, air. Remember, ten have died building freedom's hope across the mighty avenues of America.

ON THE *CONTRARY,* MARGO -- IT'S A *CODE!* AND IT GIVES US THE FIRST PART OF THE *PUZZLE!*

TO THE *COBALT CLUB,* SHREVVY!

BUT... IT'S NO MORE THAN A *SLOGAN* ...A *BADLY WRITTEN* ONE!.

TIPPED BY THE THREE-WORD SALUTATION, THE SHADOW HAS READ EVERY THIRD WORD: "GUN/ARRIVE/WATER. TEN/BUILDING/ACROSS/AVENUES."

AN HOUR LATER, ON A SWANK, MID-MANHATTAN SIDE STREET, THE BEAUTIFUL *MARGO LANE* STEPS FROM THE CAB, ACCOMPANIED BY A SUAVE GENTLEMAN KNOWN AS *LAMONT CRANSTON!*

GO AHEAD, MARGO! I'LL JOIN YOU *SHORTLY!*

ALL RIGHT, LAMONT!

THEN, IN THE FOYER OF NEW YORK'S MOST *EXCLUSIVE* CLUB, CRANSTON DIALS A NUMBER NOT LISTED IN ANY DIRECTORY...

...AND SOMEWHERE IN THE CITY, A HUSKY VOICE *ANSWERS!*

BURBANK TALKING!

As Cranston idly drifts toward his table, a chance remark from a dining club-member causes him to suppress a smile...

Meanwhile, in the upper east-side apartment building owned by one *Harry Vincent*...

HA HA HA HA

AAAGH!

BOSS, YOU'VE JUST GIVEN ME A *LESSON* IN THE ART OF *CLOBBERING!* YOU DIDN'T EVEN DRAW YOUR *WEAPONS!*

FOR TWO SUCH AS *THESE?* IT WOULD BE LIKE USING A *REGIMENT* TO DEFEAT A PAIR OF *MICE!*

I'M TAKING THIS SPECIMEN TO THE *LAB!* YOU DELIVER HIS COHORT TO THE *LAW!*

WILL *DO!*

HORRIBLY FRIGHTENED, THE HOODLUM BLINKS TO WAKEFULNESS AND FINDS HIMSELF SEEMINGLY....*FLOATING* IN A VAST OVAL OF BLUE GLOW!

HE CAN SEE NEITHER WALLS NOR CEILING....HEAR *NOTHING*--

---EXCEPT A STEELY *COMMAND*--

GAZE INTO MY *RING*... MY *GIRASOL*--

...LET THE FIERY DEPTHS *ENGULF* YOU! YOUR WILL IS AS THE SPRING SNOWS, MELTING, MELTING...

...YOU ARE *POWERLESS* TO RESIST ME!

Y-YES

19

SPEAK! BARE YOUR **THOUGHTS!**

SIX MONTHS AGO... STEAL PLANS FOR NEW KIND OF SHIP FROM NAVY HEADQUARTERS...

...TONIGHT, RELEASE PRISONERS...

AND THE NAME OF YOUR **LEADER?**

DON'T KNOW... INSTRUCTIONS AND PAYMENT BY MAIL...IN CODE...ANOTHER JOB TOMORROW NIGHT...

...AT ELEVEN...

NOW **SLEEP!** YOU WILL AWAKEN BEHIND **BARS!**

YOU DIDN'T GET MUCH **INFORMATION** FROM HIM, DID YOU?

BUT I **DID,** MARGO!

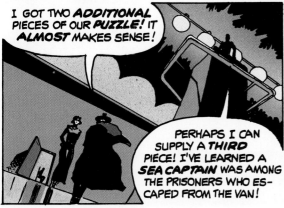

I GOT TWO **ADDITIONAL** PIECES OF OUR **PUZZLE!** IT **ALMOST** MAKES SENSE!

PERHAPS I CAN SUPPLY A **THIRD** PIECE! I'VE LEARNED A **SEA CAPTAIN** WAS AMONG THE PRISONERS WHO ES-CAPED FROM THE VAN!

AN ARMY OF CRIMINALS...STOLEN SHIP PLANS...AND A **SEAMAN!** YES--THE PATTERN BEGINS TO REVEAL ITSELF!

BURBANK-- CALL **SHREVVY.** I HAVE **INSTRUCTIONS** FOR HIM!

EARLY THE NEXT AFTERNOON, LAMONT CRANSTON VISITS **WALL STREET**...

SECOND · NATIONAL · BANK.

...AND GREETS FINANCIER **OSGOOD BAMBER**--

LAMONT, LADDIE!--WORRIED ABOUT YOUR **INVESTMENTS?**

NOT A **BIT,** OSGOOD! THEY'RE SAFE IN YOUR CARE! NO, I HAPPENED TO BE IN THE **NEIGHBORHOOD**--

--AND FRANKLY, I HOPED YOU'D LET ME IN ON THE **SECRET!** I'VE HEARD **RUMORS** OF BIG **EXCITEMENT** ON THE STREET!

THE WORD **DOES** GET OUT, DOESN'T IT? WELL, LAD...DON'T GET **ALARMED!**

TRUTH IS, WE'RE SHIPPING A LOT OF WORN-OUT **CURRENCY** TO WASHINGTON SOON!

--MONEY THAT'S TOO **USED** TO BE GOOD!

I'M SUPERVISING THE TRANSFER **MYSELF**--!

QUITE A **TEMPTATION**... FOR A **THIEF!** AREN'T YOU **WORRIED?**

NOT AT **ALL!**

THE SHIPMENT WILL BE IN **ARMORED CARS** GUARDED BY A **CONVOY** OF **SOLDIERS**...

--AND **BESIDES,** NO ONE EXCEPT THE BOYS IN **WASHINGTON** AND I KNOW THE **ROUTE** THE SHIPMENT WILL TAKE!

NO, LAD, THAT CASH IS SAFE AS *HOUSES*!

THANKS FOR THE *CHAT*, OSGOOD! SEE YOU!

DO ANY *GOOD*, BOSS?

THE FINAL PIECES OF THE PUZZLE ARE IN *PLACE*, SHREVVY!

TO *HEAD-QUARTERS--QUICKLY!* THERE IS MUCH TO DO BEFORE NIGHTFALL--

--*NIGHTFALL*...IT IS AS THOUGH A GIANT HAND SNATCHED AWAY THE LIGHT THIS COOL SPRING EVENING, SO ABRUPT IS THE DARKNESS! BUT THERE IS *MOVEMENT*... ACTIVITY...

...IN LOWER MANHATTAN, A COMPANY OF TROOPERS LOAD A MILLION DOLLARS WORTH OF SHABBY BILLS INTO ARMORED VEHICLES UNDER THE WATCHFUL GAZE OF *OSGOOD BAMBER*....

...THROUGH THE STREETS THEY RUMBLE, BOUND FOR THE *TREASURY BUILDING* IN THE NATION'S CAPITAL...

...AND THERE IS ALSO *EVIL* ABROAD THIS EVENING...

THEM *ARMY* GUYS OUGHTTA BE ALONG IN A COUPLA MINUTES! BETTER GET *READY*!

24

MAYBE *THEY'RE* FOOLS -- BUT NOT *ME!* I'M OVER *HERE* ...WHERE YA CAN'T REACH ME BEFORE I LET *MOONLIGHT* INTA YA!

OWWWW! ---MY *SHOULDER!*

KRAK

EXCELLENT *MARKSMANSHIP* ...THOUGH NOT *NEC-ESSARY!* I COULD HAVE SHOT THE TOMMY GUN FROM HIS HANDS --*EASILY!*

WELL...I NEEDED THE *PRACTICE!*

OUR WORK IS *FINISHED,* SHADOW?

NO! THESE ARE *SMALL FRY*...WHOM THE POLICE ARE COMING TO *NET!* OUR *MAJOR* TASK LIES *AHEAD*--!

WHY? THE MONEY SHIPMENT IS *ALREADY* CROSSING THE BRIDGE!

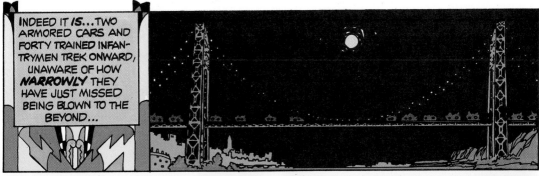

INDEED IT *IS*...TWO ARMORED CARS AND FORTY TRAINED INFANTRYMEN TREK ONWARD, UNAWARE OF HOW *NARROWLY* THEY HAVE JUST MISSED BEING BLOWN TO THE BEYOND...

...UNAWARE, TOO, OF THE AIRCRAFT BEARING THEIR *SAVIOR*, HOVERING ABOVE THE WINE-DARK WATER...

THE *REAL* CULPRITS ARE STILL AT LARGE, MARGO! WE CAN NOT PERMIT THEM TO ROAM *FREE*..

...PERHAPS TO SCHEME *FURTHER!*

UNLESS I'VE MISCALCULATED *BADLY*, THEY SHOULD BE PASSING UNDER US AT THIS VERY *MOMENT!*

WHERE? THERE'S *NOTHING* ON THE RIVER!

NOT *ON* THE RIVER-- I SAID *UNDER* IT!

BURBANK SPOKE TO OUR ASSOCIATE IN THE *NAVY* AND LEARNED THAT BLUEPRINTS FOR A *SUBMARINE* WERE STOLEN SIX MONTHS AGO!

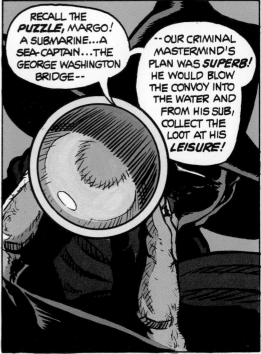

RECALL THE *PUZZLE*, MARGO! A SUBMARINE...A SEA-CAPTAIN...THE GEORGE WASHINGTON BRIDGE--

--OUR CRIMINAL MASTERMIND'S PLAN WAS *SUPERB!* HE WOULD BLOW THE CONVOY INTO THE WATER AND FROM HIS SUB, COLLECT THE LOOT AT HIS *LEISURE!*

26

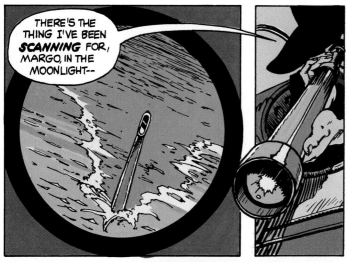

THERE'S THE THING I'VE BEEN *SCANNING* FOR, MARGO, IN THE MOONLIGHT--

-- A *PERISCOPE*... A DEVICE SUBMARINE CREWS USE FOR LOCATING THEIR *VICTIMS!*

...*EXCEPT...THIS* TIME *THEY'LL* BE THE VICTIMS! HOLD THE CONTROLS STEADY--

--WHILE I RELEASE THESE *DEPTH BOMBS!*

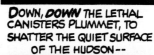

DOWN, *DOWN* THE LETHAL CANISTERS PLUMMET, TO SHATTER THE QUIET SURFACE OF THE HUDSON--

...AND, WITHIN A FEW SECONDS, SEND A SPOUT ERUPTING *UPWARD,* AS HUNDREDS OF POUNDS OF EXPLOSIVES BURST IN THE MURKY DEEP!

KA-WHUMP

WITH A HISS AND A GURGLE, THE CRAFT SLOWLY EMERGES, AND A DAZED GUNMAN CLIMBS ONTO THE DECK...

...TO BE FOLLOWED BY HIS *FELLOWS*--

THE ENGINES ARE DAMAGED BEYOND *REPAIR!* WE'LL HAVETA *SWIM* FOR IT---!

ANY IDEA *WHY* BEDLAM BROKE LOOSE, CAP'N?

YOU CALL IT *BEDLAM*--

--ANOTHER MIGHT CALL IT *BLASTING POWDER*--

--AND *I* CALL IT *VENGEANCE*--

FINALLY... IN THE LAST GLOOM-LADEN HOUR BEFORE DAWN, A FRANTIC MAN SCURRIES FROM HIS LAVISH MANSION, HIS ARM ALREADY ACHING FROM THE WEIGHT OF AN OVERSTUFFED *SUITCASE*...

TAXI! TAXI!

WHERE *TO*, MAC?

THE *RAILROAD STATION!* QUICKLY -- I HAVE A FIVE O'CLOCK *TRAIN* TO CATCH!

RUNNING FROM YOUR EVIL *DEEDS*, OSGOOD BAMBER? RUNNING FROM YOUR ATTEMPT TO *STEAL*...AND *MURDER?*

H-HOW DO *YOU* KNOW--?

YOU TOLD LAMONT CRANSTON ONLY *YOU* KNEW THE ROUTE THE SHIPMENT WAS TO TAKE! ONLY YOU KNEW TIMES--AND PLACES!

YOU KNEW THESE THINGS *SIX MONTHS AGO*, WHEN YOU HAD THE *SUBMARINE* DIAGRAMS STOLEN!

SO *YOU* MASTERMINDED THE *ROBBERY* I FOILED!

WHO-- *ARE* YOU?

ONE WHO *LOATHES* SMALL, GREEDY CREATURES WHO PREY ON DECENT MEN--

From the Shadow's Private Files

The Shadow

AGAINST THE GAUDY BACKGROUND OF THE *CARNIVAL*, THE *HARLEQUIN* PLAYS HIS GRIM GAME OF *DEATH*! WHO *IS* THE MURDER FIEND IN THE GAY GARB...?

BENZARE...A KNIFE-THROWER WITH A *NASTY* TEMPER!

SPIDORA... BODY OF AN *INSECT*, HEAD OF A LOVELY *WOMAN*!

NICCO.... ARE CIGARETTES HIS *ONLY* VICE?

DAMON *and* PYTHIAS... THE INSEPARABLE TWINS!

ALHAMBRA... SNAKES ARE HER ONLY FRIENDS!

PANCHINI... DOES THE HARLEQUIN'S COSTUME HIDE HIS *TATTOOS*?

AJAX... IS HE AS MAD AS HE *SEEMS*?

POP SORBER...A BOSS WITH A NEED FOR *MONEY*!

ONLY A MOCKING, DISTANT *LAUGH* SEEMS TO KNOW THE KILLER'S IDENTITY!

FREAK SHOW MURDERS

A REMOTE MANSION SOMEWHERE IN SOUTH CAROLINA...AND A SLEEK *ROADSTER* SPEEDING THROUGH THE DUSK...

FROM THE CAR STEPS A YOUNG, ATHLETIC-LOOKING MAN, AND...

I'M *STEVE KILROY!* MISTER TREFT IS *EXPECTING* ME!

THIS *WAY,* SIR!

THEN...

MISTER *MILTON TREFT?* I HAVE A CHECK FOR *ONE MILLION DOLLARS!* IT'S *YOURS,* PROVIDED THE PRODUCT IS ALL YOU *CLAIM!*

SEE FOR *YOURSELF!* THAT *STATUE* IS *PURE ALUMITE!* GO ON..., LIFT IT!

...AMAZING!--A LIFE-SIZED *SCULPTURE* WEIGHING ONLY *OUNCES!*

AND WITH THE TENSILE STRENGTH OF *STEEL!*

THE FORMULA FOR THIS IS *WORTH* THE MILLION!

THERE *IS* NO FORMULA, KILROY! THE MAN WHO INVENTED ALUMITE *DIED* BEFORE WRITING ANYTHING DOWN!

THERE IS JUST THE STATUE YOU HOLD! BUT I'M SURE YOUR COMPANY'S CHEMISTS WILL BE ABLE TO DEDUCE THE *SECRET!*

HERE'S YOUR PAYMENT--

HE CAN TAKE THE CHECK! I'LL TAKE THE STATUE!

WHO ARE YOU--?

CALL ME THE HARLEQUIN-- AND GIVE ME WHAT I'VE COME FOR!

YOU CLOWN! IF YOU SERIOUSLY THINK I'LL LET YOU BARGE IN MAKING DEMANDS--

TREFT! WATCH OUT! HE ISN'T KIDDING!

WADDLING OLD FOOL!

BLAMM

HE'LL KILL ME, TOO-- UNLESS I CAN...

...ESCAPE!

SO INTENT IS STEVE KILROY ON FLIGHT, HE DOES NOT NOTICE A GRIM-VISAGED FORM EMERGE FROM THE BLACKNESS...

HA HA HA HA HA HA HA HA HA HA HA

...NOR DOES HE HEAR A MARROW-CHILLING LAUGH...

HURRY! PUT THE STATUE IN THE TRUCK AND--

HA HA HA HA HA HA HA

Y-YOU HEAR *THAT?*

YEAH... AND I FEEL SAFER WITH A FISTFUL OF *GUN!*

DROP YOUR *WEAPONS!*

THERE HE IS! *BLAST* 'IM...

UNNGH!

BLAM!

PANIC-STRICKEN, THE GUNMAN FIRES WILDLY AT WHERE THE BLACK-CLOAKED FIGURE *WAS*--

BLAM BLAM BLAM BLAM

HUH--?

THUD

HIS WORK *DONE*, THE STRANGE, DEADLY FORM MELTS INTO THE NIGHT...

...AND SOON, IN A ROADSIDE DINER, A SPLENDIDLY CLAD MAN DIALS A NUMBER LISTED IN *NO DIRECTORY!* IN A LOW VOICE, HE SPEAKS...

BURBANK! I ARRIVED TOO *LATE!* I CAUGHT THE *SMALL FRY*--

-- BUT IN THE BATTLE, THE *BIG FISH* GOT AWAY WITH HIS *PRIZE!* TELL MARGO TO JOIN THE *SORBER CARNIVAL* IN *TITUSVILLE!*

CONSIDER IT *DONE*, CHIEF!

HE SAYS YOU'RE TO--

I *HEARD!* I'M TO HOOK UP WITH A *CARNIVAL*, EH? I WONDER *WHY?*

WELL, ONE THING'S CERTAIN-- HE HAS A GOOD *REASON!* HE ALWAYS *DOES!*

SO, THE FOLLOWING EVENING, *MARGO LANE* FINDS HERSELF ON A GARISH *MIDWAY* NEAR A SMALL SOUTHERN TOWN...

QUICKLY, SHE LOCATES THE OWNER AND, DISGUISING HER REFINED SPEECH, CALLS COARSELY--

YOU *POP SORBER?* I'M LOOKIN' FOR A *JOB!*

YER IN *LUCK*, MISSY! I NEED A LADY *FREAK!*

AW--DON'T *WORRY!* I AIN'T GONNA AST YA TO CUT OFF YER EARS OR NOTHIN' --

--ALL YA GOTTA DO IS STICK YOUR HEAD THROUGH A *HOLE* IN THE BACK OF A BOOTH--

--AND PRETEND TO BE *SPIDORA,* THE HUMAN *SPIDER!*

SOUNDS *REAL* EASY! YOU GOT A *DEAL,* POP!

C'MON ,,, I'LL INTRODUCE YA *AROUND!*

HERE'S OUR *TATTOOED MAN--PANCHINI!*

THIS WALKING *ART GALLERY* IS PLEASED TO MEET YOU!

NOW, MEET *ALHAMBRA,* QUEEN OF THE *SNAKES...* AND BEHIND HER, *BENZARE,* THE *KNIFE THROWER.*

WE MUST GET TOGETHER FOR SOME *GIRL TALK,* DEARIE!

I, *TOO,* WISH TO GET TOGETHER WITH THE BEAUTEOUS WOMAN--

--FOR MORE *INTIMATE* PURPOSES!

I AWAIT YOUR *PLEASURE!*

SWELL... LONG AS YOU'RE NOT HOLDING YOUR *BREATH!*

AND, AFTER THE FINAL PERFORMANCE OF THE EVENING...

I NEVER THOUGHT IT WOULD BE SO *HARD* TO SIT AND LET PEOPLE *STARE* AT ME!

SOMEONE'S MOVING OUTSIDE THE *TENT*--

--AND IT'S THE VERY MAN I'M *LOOKING* FOR!

YOU!

AJAX ISN'T YOUR *REAL* NAME--!

YOU'VE BEEN SENT TO *GET* ME-- YOU *WON'T!*

MY, MY! AREN'T WE *FIERCE!*

AS A *WILD MAN*, YOU'RE A *BUST*--

--BUT AS A *JUDO PARTNER*--

--YOU'RE *PERFECT!* YOU *FALL* SO NICELY!

OWWW!

YOU'RE *REALLY* STEVE KILROY, AREN'T YOU?

AND YOU'RE A *POLICEWOMAN?* I'LL GO *QUIETLY*... BUT I *DIDN'T* KILL TREFT!

OF *COURSE* YOU'RE NO *KILLER!* AND I'M NOT *POLICE...* I'VE BEEN SENT TO *HELP* YOU!

SENT? BY WHO?

HHAHA HA HA HA

HA HA HA HA

MISS LANE IS AN ASSOCIATE OF... THE *SHADOW,* STEVE KILROY!

I REASONED YOU *HAD* TO BE WITH THE SORBER SHOWS! YOU *VANISHED* TWO NIGHTS AGO...

...AND THIS CARNIVAL WAS IN THE *AREA!* YOU WERE *FRIGHTENED!* YOU SOUGHT *REFUGE...* AND *DISGUISE!*

UNLESS I AM *MISTAKEN--* AND I *SELDOM* AM--YOU WERE NOT THE *ONLY* ONE WHO LEFT THE TREFT ESTATE FOR THESE TENTS--!

YOU MEAN THE WEIRDO IN THE *COSTUME--* THAT *HARLEQUIN* FELLOW IS *ALSO...?*

BAMB!

SHADOW... THAT WAS A *SHOT!*

IT CAME FROM *ALHAMBRA'S* WAGON...

...WHERE'D HE *GO?*

40

SILENTLY, *SWIFTLY*, HE CROSSES THE LOT...

...ONLY TO ARRIVE AT THE SNAKE WOMAN'S WAGON *TOO LATE!*

WHO *DID* THIS? *WHO?*

...SAW HIM...IN *CLOWN* SUIT... TOOK OFF HIS... MASK,...AND IT WAS-- *AHHHHHH!*

WITH A SOFT SIGH, THE SNAKE WOMAN DIES...

SHE WAS *MURDERED* BECAUSE SHE ACCIDENTALLY LEARNED THE *HARLEQUIN'S IDENTITY!*

THE POOR THING--!

...ER--*PARDON ME!* I SAW HIM HEADING TOWARD THE PLACE WHERE THEY PARKED THE BIG *STUFFED WHALE!*

I CAN CALL THE *SHERIFF* AND...

...WHERE'D HE *GO?*

TO CATCH A *FIEND!*

YES, SILENTLY AND SWIFTLY HE MOVES,,, TO CATCH A *FIEND*--

FLAME SPITS FROM THE DIRECTION OF THE GIGANTIC BEAST--!

BLAM

PUZZLED, THE PIEBALD CRIMINAL STEPS FORWARD AND PEERS AROUND--

--AND IS *FROZEN* BY AN ICY *COMMAND*!

DROP YOUR *WEAPON*-- OR BE SERVED AS YOU SERVED *ALHAMBRA*!

AND REMOVE YOUR *MASK*!

BOY O BOY, YOU ARE *SOMETHING*, SHADOW! YOU *CAUGHT* THE RAT! I'LL ADMIT,,,

,,,I'D *NEVER* HAVE BEEN ABLE TO--

THEN--

--OOOPS!

--THE HAPLESS STEVE KILROY'S FOOT CATCHES ON A *TENT ROPE*--

42

--BRINGING A CANVAS SHROUD DOWN ON THE WHALE... AND THE *SHADOW!*

HE *SCRAMMED!*

HEH HEH-- *SORRY!*

MEANWHILE, IN ALHAMBRA'S QUARTERS...

SHE WAS A *GOOD ATTRACTION!* WE'LL *MISS* HER!

YEAH, SHE WAS *OKAY!*

NONSENSE! THE WOMAN WAS *VILE--* HER AND HER *SNAKES!*

HOWEVER, I REALIZE THIS BUSINESS MUST HAVE UPSET YOU, M'LOVELY! I'LL ESCORT YOU TO SOMEPLACE...*PRIVATE!*

A GLASS OF WINE... SOFT MUSIC--

WOULD YOU CARE TO *LET GO?*

OOOO--WF!

CHUD

--THANKS!

GROWLING WITH *FURY*, BENZARE JERKS A *KNIFE* FROM UNDER HIS JACKET...

MISERABLE *WENCH*--

...ONLY TO HAVE THE BLADE SNAPPED FROM HIS FINGERS BY A *BULLET*--!

NEXT TIME, FRIEND, I'LL AIM *DIFFERENTLY!* -- YOU'RE *WARNED!*

I WANT *ALL* OF YOU IN THE MAIN TENT IN *FIVE MINUTES!* BE THERE...OR REGRET IT FOR THE REST OF YOUR *SHORT* LIFE!

HE'S *GONE!* ...SAY -- WHO *IS* HE?

I DUNNO... BUT THE WAY HE *TALKS*-- I *LISTEN!* ONLY ONE THING--

-- I HOPE HE MAKES IT *QUICK!* THE TRAIN THAT WILL CARRY US TO OUR NEXT STOP IS *WAITING!*

I DISCOVERED THE TRICK *EARLIER*--AS *NICCO!*

SO *THIS* BIRD'S BEEN CAUSING MY GRIEF! WAIT TILL I GET MY *HANDS* ON HIM--

STEVE... NO! YOU'RE IN THE LINE OF *FIRE!*

ONE *MOVE*-- FROM *ANY- ONE*-- AND I'LL SPLATTER HIS BRAINS ON THE FLOOR!

HE'S GETTING *AWAY*-- AGAIN!

HE'LL GO TO JOIN HIS *BROTHER*-- AND I KNOW WHERE THE SECOND TWIN *HAS* TO BE!

THE TWINS ARE *FOREIGN AGENTS,* SENT TO OBTAIN A SAMPLE OF THE *MIRACLE METAL* --*ALUMITE!*

THEIR *PROBLEM* IS TO HIDE THE ALUMITE *STATUE* UNTIL THEY REACH THE *COAST*-- A *LARGE* STATUE, REMEMBER!

THERE IS ONLY *ONE PLACE* IN THE SHOW THEY COULD *SAFELY* CONCEAL IT!

47

48

49

50

WIND *TEARING* AT THEM, THESE TWO CLOSE IN A FINAL, FIERCE *STRUGGLE*...

THE *STATUE*... IT'S *FALLING*--

DESPERATELY, THE HARLEQUIN *LURCHES*, HIS MOMENTUM CARRYING HIM OUT OF THE RACING CAB--

--TO HIS *DOOM!*

HA HA HA HA HA HA HA HA

THE SHADOW *NEVER* FAILS!

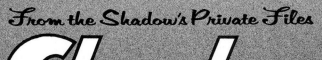

From the Shadow's Private Files

The Shadow

FROM THE DARKEST HEART OF THE CITY HE CAME... A TWISTED, VICIOUS **TRAVESTY** OF A HUMAN BEING... AN UTTERLY **RUTHLESS** MOBSTER WITH THE SOUL OF A **SERPENT** AND MORALS TO MATCH--AND A MASTER PLAN THAT ONLY THE **SHADOW** COULD HOPE TO THWART...

COME WITH THE MYSTERIOUS ENEMY OF EVIL AS HE FOLLOWS A BLOOD-SPATTERED TRAIL TO...

The **KINGDOM** of the **COBRA**

52

QUIET...AND *COLD*,,,MIDNIGHT LAYS UPON THE CITY LIKE AN INKY *CLOAK!* MOST *GOOD* PEOPLE ARE TUCKED INTO THEIR BEDS--

--HOWEVER, THE *BAD* ARE ABOUT THEIR DEEDS,,,AS IN THIS SUBURBAN BANK,,,

SNAP IT *UP*, BLUE JAW! I AIN'T MAKIN' A *CAREER* OF ONE LOUSY JOB!

I'M AN *ARTIST* AN' YA CAN'T HURRY *ART!*

ME, I DON'T KNOW FROM *ART*--

--BUT I KNOW WHAT I *LIKE!*

SUCH AS THAT *VAULT* BLOWIN', HUH?

KA-WNMPH

GRAB THE *BIG* BILLS-- AN' BE *QUICK!*

SHHHH,,, YOU BIRDS *HEAR* SOMETHIN'?

THAT *LAUGH*... GOIN' THROUGH ME LIKE AN *ICE PICK!*

HA HA HA HA HA HA HA

COULD IT BE,,, *HIM?*

T-THE *SHADOW*--!

54

A MOMENT LATER...

NOTHIN' IN SIGHT 'CEPT THAT *CAB!* I'M *SAFE*--

UGGMF!

T-THOD

ANY *PROBLEMS?*

NO, MARGO...

...NONE AT *ALL!* THE STOOL-PIGEON GAVE US EXACT INFORMATION--THE TIME, THE TOWN AND THE *BANK* THOSE HOODS PLANNED TO ROB!

ONE THING IS *PUZZLING,* THOUGH! THE *LEADER* IS... ER-- *WAS* A MOBSTER NAMED *BLUE JAW GRADY*--

--AND TO THE BEST OF MY KNOWLEDGE, GRADY SHOULD BE SERVING A *TWENTY-YEAR* STRETCH AT *AINSLEY PRISON!*

THEN, AT A PLACE WHICH DOES NOT *OFFICIALLY EXIST*--

BURBANK! GET THE WARDEN OF AINSLEY PRISON ON THE TELEPHONE!

AS YOU *SAY,* SHADOW!

HE'S ON THE *LINE!*

AH *WARDEN*, ME BOY! THIS'S *TIM O'SHAUGNESSY*, REPORTER FOR THE *NEW YORK TRIBUNE!* I'M CALLIN' TO ASK AFTER ONE OF YOUR *PRISONERS*--

--A BOYO NAME OF *GRADY!* IS HE STILL ENJOYIN' YOUR *HOSPITALITY?*

HE IS *INDEED*, MR. O'SHAUGNESSY! WHY DO YOU *ASK?*

JUST CHECKIN' A *STORY!* THANKS AN' *BYE!*

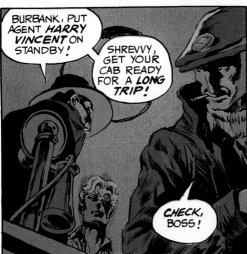

BURBANK, PUT AGENT *HARRY VINCENT* ON STANDBY!

SHREVVY, GET YOUR CAB READY FOR A *LONG TRIP!*

CHECK, BOSS!

AND *MARGO*-- I HAVE A *SPECIAL* TASK FOR YOU! LISTEN ,,,

EARLY THE NEXT MORNING, A TAXI STOPS IN FRONT OF THE GRIM, GRAY WALLS OF *AINSLEY PRISON*--

-- AND *MARGO LANE* GETS OUT ,,, BUT NOT A MARGO ANY OF HER FRIENDS *WOULD RECOGNIZE*--

YOUNG MAN, I'M *AGATHA FLUT* OF THE WOMEN'S JAIL REFORM CLUB! I DEMAND TO INSPECT THE PREMISES *IMMEDIATELY!*

56

AND, INSIDE THE FORBIDDING STRUCTURE...

OOOOO...*FILTHY! DISGRACEFUL!* GUARD, I *INSIST* ON SEEING THE *WARDEN!*

HERE HE COMES *NOW,* MA'AM!

CAN I *HELP* YOU, MISS FLUT?

YOU CERTAINLY *CAN!* LEAD ME TO A TELEPHONE THIS *INSTANT!*

NO *PROBLEM--*

--YOU CAN USE THE ONE IN MY *OFFICE!*

I PREFER TO MAKE MY CALL *ALONE!*

AS THE DOOR CLOSES BEHIND HER, MARGO DIALS AN *UNLISTED NUMBER* AND...

HELLO...*BURBANK!* THE SHADOW WAS *RIGHT!* SOMETHING'S DRASTICALLY *WRONG--*

-- NONE OF THE CELLS ARE *LOCKED!* THE MAN WHO'S SUPPOSED TO BE THE *WARDEN--*

CLIK

--IF HE'S A *PRISON OFFICIAL,* I'M *FANNY BRICE!* I *RECOGNIZED* HIM!--HE'S *REALLY A MOBSTER...*

58

MEANWHILE, IN *CENTRAL PARK*--

HARRY, POOCHUMS, I FEEL SIMPLY *GIRLISH* WITH YOU!

WHY DON'T WE GO TO *MY* PLACE AND LOOK AT MY HIGH SCHOOL *YEARBOOK*?

SORRY, DOLL! I GOT FISH TO *FRY* AND KITES TO *FLY!* CATCH YOU *NEXT WEEK*, MAYBE!

WHAT'S THE *PROGRAM*, BOSS?

FIRST, A CHANGE OF *CLOTHING* AND *IDENTITY!* THEN A *JOURNEY!*

I'LL GIVE YOU INSTRUCTIONS ON THE *WAY!*

SO, AS EVENING CREEPS ACROSS THE LAND...

OPEN THE *GATE*, CHUM! I GOT A *CUSTOMER* FOR YOUR LITTLE *HOTEL!*

BRING HIM *IN!*

I'LL SHOW HIM TO HIS ...*ROOM!*

NO SENSE YOU STICKIN' *AROUND*, PALLY!

OHH, I DUNNO... I LIKE THE COUNTRY *AIR!* MAKES ME SORTA *SLEEPY*--

--YOU *TOO*, HUH?

KWOP

HE OUGHT TO SNOOZE LONG ENOUGH FOR ME TO *PLANT* THIS STUFF--!

AND THE SOONER THE *BETTER*--

--ONE SMALL *ACCIDENT* AND IT'LL BE RAINING HARRY VINCENT FOR *DAYS*!

GENERATOR ROOM

ELSEWHERE,,,

YOU AIN'T GONNA MIND OUR JOINT A *BIT*! WE MANAGE TO HAVE A FEW *LAUGHS*!

BOYS, MEET YOUR NEW *ROOMMATE*!

HOWDY, BUD!

WELCOME!

HE'S *CUTE*!

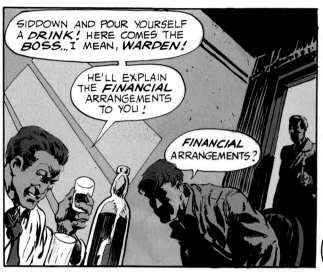

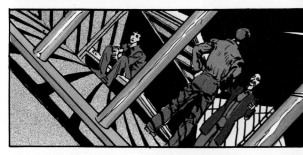

HE FREED THE... INMATES, AND, AND...

...AND SIMPLY *TOOK OVER,* EH? A NEAT SCHEME...A *VICIOUS* SCHEME...AND ONE FOR WHICH HE'LL PAY THE *FINAL* PRICE!

I'D LIKE TO *BELIEVE* YOU...BUT BY THE TIME ANYONE *LEARNS* WHAT HE'S DONE...

--HE'LL BE *GONE* ...AND WE'LL BE *DEAD!*

THE *CANDLE*... IT'S BURNED OUT!

IN THE DIM RAYS OF THE COLD WHITE MOON SHINING THROUGH THE BARRED WINDOW, A STARTLING *TRANSFORMATION* TAKES PLACE... THE NEWCOMER *VANISHES* ABRUPTLY--

-- IN HIS *PLACE*, A SLOUCH-HATTED *AVENGER* WHO REMOVES A SLIM METAL DEVICE FROM A HOLLOW TOOTH--

--AND APPLIES IT TO THE *LOCK*--

--WITH *ASTONISHING* RESULTS...

UNBELIEVABLE! THAT DOOR IS GUARANTEED *PICK-PROOF!*

ARE YOU... THE PERSON I *THINK* YOU ARE--?

PROBABLY! WAIT HERE FOR ME! I SHOULDN'T BE *LONG!*

SWIFT AND SILENT AS A WIND-DRIVEN *CLOUD*, HE GLIDES ALONG THE CORRIDOR, MERGING WITH THE DARKNESS--

--REAPPEARING BEFORE *KING COBRA'S* OFFICE! THE WALLS ECHO HIS *COMMAND*--

PREPARE YOURSELF, COBRA! PREPARE TO *SURRENDER*-- OR *DIE!*

WARDEN

THERE'S A *THIRD* POSSIBILITY--

--THAT *YOU* WILL SURRENDER ,,,OR WATCH THIS LOVELY CREATURE END IN A PARTICU-LARLY *HORRIBLE* MANNER!

YOU'LL NOTICE I'M DRENCHING HER WITH *GASOLINE*--!

NOW, I HAVE ONLY TO FLICK AN *ASH* AND WE'LL HAVE THE PLEASURE OF HEARING HER *SCREAM* AS THE FLAMES CONSUME HER!

YOUR *DECISION!* DROP YOUR GUNS, OR...

YOU WIN-- *THIS* ROUND!

YOU *DISAPPOINT* ME, SHADOW! I WAS *CERTAIN* YOU'D SACRIFICE THE LIFE OF A WOMAN--ALBEIT A *BEAUTIFUL* ONE--IN ORDER TO BAG SUCH A PRIZE AS *ME!*

I *MIGHT*-- IF IT WERE *NECESSARY!*

66

PRETTY *NIFTY!* I SLIPPED FROM MY ROPES AND...

WE CAN CONGRATULATE OURSELVES *LATER,* MARGO! OUR TASK IS NOT YET *FINISHED!*

THE LEADER *ESCAPED* IN THE FRAY!

I'LL PURSUE *COBRA* WHILE YOU SUMMON THE POLICE TO CAPTURE THE *MOB!*

NO SENSE IN ASKING HIM TO BE *CAREFUL--*

WITHIN *MOMENTS,* THE AVENGER JOINS HIS AIDE IN THE YARD AND...

HAS ANYONE *PASSED* YOU, HARRY?

YEAH--A BIRD RUNNING LIKE HIS UNDERWEAR WAS ON *FIRE--*

I CUT HIM OFF FROM THE *GATE,* SO HE WENT IN *THERE...,* WHERE I *BLASTED!*

I GUESS HE'S *TRAPPED...,* BUT I WOULDN'T *FOLLOW* HIM FOR ALL THE TEA IN *CHINA!*

THE PROBLEM IS, I SET *TWO* CHARGES TO GO OFF AT MIDNIGHT... AND ONLY *ONE* DID!

WHICH MEANS A DOZEN STICKS OF HIGH-GRADE *TNT* ARE SITTING IN THE RUBBLE--

--AND ANY *SECOND* THEY'LL BLOW THAT HEAP OF STONE *SKY-HIGH!*

FORGET HIM, CHIEF! HE *CAN'T* ESCAPE!

NO!

I *NEVER* LEAVE A JOB *HALF DONE!*

AND, IN THE CRUMPLED STRUCTURE...

AGAIN, I DEMAND YOUR *SURRENDER,* COBRA!

AGAIN, I *REFUSE!* I REALIZE I'M *FINISHED,* BECAUSE OF *YOU!*

MY LAST DEED ON THE EARTH WILL BE AN ACT OF *REVENGE*... AS IS *FITTING!* I'VE FOUND *THIS* -- ENOUGH EXPLOSIVE TO RIP US BOTH TO *BITS!*

70

THE SHADOW *NEVER* FAILS!

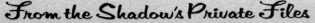

The Shadow

NIGHT... AND THIS LONELY COUNTRY ROAD SEEMS TO STRETCH BEYOND TIME, BEYOND LIFE ITSELF...INTO *ETERNITY--!* THIS IS A HUSH, BROKEN ONLY BY THE THRUM OF A POWERFUL TRUCK ENGINE...

19
S.F. HICKMAN

YET...*WAIT!* BE STILL...AND FEEL THE PHANTOM PRESENCE OF ONE WHO HATES *EVIL*... A BLACK-CAPED *AVENGER* SILENTLY, STEADILY STALKING HIS *PREY!*

WAIT...FOR IN A MOMENT THE HUSH WILL BE SHATTERED WITH AN ACT OF *VIOLENCE*--AND THE BEGINNING OF A HARSH *JUSTICE*...

DEATH IS BLISS

76

YOU *HEARD,* BOSS?

I *DID!* ODD... JOHNSON IS THE *FIFTH* HOODLUM TO MEET AN ACCIDENTAL DEATH THIS YEAR!

PERHAPS *CHANCE* IS DOING MY WORK *FOR ME!*

SOON, IN A PLACE THAT *HAS* NO ADDRESS...

YOU HAVE *ORDERS,* SHADOW?

YES, BURBANK! WRITE THIS *LICENSE NUMBER--K13945!* CALL OUR AGENT IN THE *STATE CAPITOL* AND FIND OUT TO WHOM IT WAS *ISSUED!*

THAT'S THE LICENSE OF THE *TRUCK* YOU STOPPED?

CORRECT! THEN CALL *MARGO LANE* AND *HARRY VINCENT!* THEY ARE TO INVESTIGATE THE TRUCK'S *OWNER!*

WHAT ABOUT *US,* BOSS?

AS LAMONT CRANSTON, FRIEND, WE SHALL VISIT THE *BLISS MISSION*--

--AND SEEK TO LEARN WHY AN INSTITUTION DEDICATED TO DESTROYING THE EVILS OF *DRINK* WAS RECEIVING A SHIPMENT OF *WHISKEY!*

FOR THE PRESENT... *LEAVE* ME!

I MUST *THINK!*

At precisely NOON the following day, an elegantly dressed gentleman steps disdainfully onto the city's FILTHIEST street--

--A boiling CALDRON of garbage, dirty pavement and unwashed flesh... where DESPAIR colors the very AIR--

GIMME DIME FOR A PINT, PALLY?

CERTAINLY NOT, DEAR FELLOW!

HELP YOU GUYS? I'M AMBROSE DEVLIN --"DEVIL" TO MY BUDDIES! I RAMROD THE MISSION!

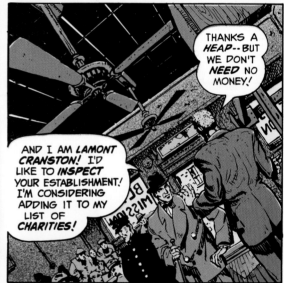

THANKS A HEAP--BUT WE DON'T NEED NO MONEY!

AND I AM LAMONT CRANSTON! I'D LIKE TO INSPECT YOUR ESTABLISHMENT! I'M CONSIDERING ADDING IT TO MY LIST OF CHARITIES!

OH, INDEED WE DON'T! I PAY THE BILLS, YES INDEEDY!

BUT I'M BEING RUDE! I HAVEN'T INTRODUCED MYSELF --I AM HOMER BLISS!

YOU FINANCE THE MISSION *ALONE,* MR. BLISS?

MY LAND, I CONSIDER MYSELF *PRIVILEGED* TO BE ABLE TO AID THESE POOR *UNFORTUNATES!*

FORGIVE ME, MR. CRANSTON... I'M *BUSY, BUSY, BUSY!* ALWAYS *RUSH, RUSH, RUSH!*

I HOPE WE MAY MEET *AGAIN!* FAREWELL!

YOU GUYS WILL BE MOVING *ON*--?

WELL ...AS LONG AS WE MADE THE *TRIP...* I'D *STILL* LIKE TO LOOK AROUND!

M-MISTER! YOU GOTTA *HELP* US...

THEY'RE KILLIN' US...

SHUT UP!

SOK

I SAW AN *OPERATING ROOM* BEHIND THAT DOOR!

FORGET IT... AND *SCRAM!*

I SAID... *SCRAM!*

YOU *DON'T* SHOVE MISTER *CRANSTON!* NEVER!

A PUNY GUY LIKE *YOU* GONNA STOP ME?

YOU'RE RUNNIN' TO *NOWHERE,* CRANSTON! THERE'S NO *EXIT* FROM THE OPERATING ROOM... NO *WINDOWS!*

KLIK

LISSEN *CLOSE,* YOU SCUMS! THE SISSY IS *TRAPPED*... AND HE'S GOT TO *DIE!* YOU'RE GONNA *FINISH* HIM WHILE I GO FIX AN *ALIBI!*

AS *REWARD,* WE'LL GIVE YOU EACH AN EXTRA BOTTLE OF THIS *HOOCH!*

THE SOONER YOU GET IT *DONE,* THE SOONER YOU'LL BE ABLE TO DRINK YOURSELVES TO *DREAMLAND!*

SLOWLY, LIKE *SLEEPWALKERS,* THE HUMAN WRECKS CLUTCH *KNIVES* AND CREEP FORWARD...

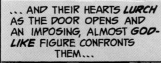

HOWEVER, A MIRTHLESS, SINISTER *SOUND* HALTS THEM IN THEIR *TRACKS*...

... AND THEIR HEARTS *LURCH* AS THE DOOR OPENS AND AN IMPOSING, ALMOST *GOD-LIKE* FIGURE CONFRONTS THEM...

...A GAZE LIKE *COLD FLAME* STABS THEIR *SOULS*...

...STRENGTH AND WILL *SEEP* FROM THEIR TORTURED BODIES...

...THEY *DARE* NOT MEET THOSE BLAZING EYES AS THE BEING WALKS IN THEIR MIDST...

...TREMBLING, IN AN *AGONY* OF TERROR, THEY STARE AT THE FLOOR...

... AND WHEN THEY CAN FINALLY MOVE...

...HE IS *GONE!*

THE AFTERNOON DIES *GRIMLY* ON LONG ISLAND THIS DAY. THICK, GRAY *CLOUDS* WASH ACROSS THE 4 P.M. SKY, CASTING A DEATHLY *PALLOR* UPON ALL THAT THEY SURVEY...

...WHICH HELPS A CERTAIN CHERUBIC GENTLEMAN'S *SALES PITCH* NOT AT ALL...

YOU'LL *LIKE* IT HERE AT *BLISSFUL GARDENS!* OH, MY LAND, INDEED YOU WILL.

I CAN THINK OF NO *BETTER* PLACE TO SPEND ONE'S *FINAL* REST! WHAT WITH THE GENTLY LAPPING WATERS OF LONG ISLAND SOUND RIGHT NEARBY TO *LULL* YOU AT NIGHTS...

SOMEHOW I DON'T THINK THE *RESIDENTS* OF THIS PLACE ARE IN ANY CONDITION TO *APPRECIATE* LAPPING WAVES, BLISS OLD BOY!

OFFICE
HOMER BLISS

OH, MY LAND, MR. VINCENT-- OF *COURSE* THEY CAN!

UPON MY WORD, AT BLISSFUL GARDENS YOUR SOUL WILL KNOW *PEACE* THAT COULD NEVER BE FOUND IN *THIS* LIFE!

83

THE MAN IS *NATCHEZ JOHNSON*...BUT ACCORDING TO BURBANK'S REPORT, HE WAS CRUSHED TO DEATH *YESTERDAY!*

YESTERDAY AIN'T *YOUR* PROBLEM, PAL! YOUR BIG WORRY IS *TOMORROW...*

WHO--?

...AN' THE FACT YOU AIN'T GONNA LIVE TO *SEE* IT!

THAT'S STILL A LOT MORE THAN *YOU'RE* GOING TO SEE, BIGSHOT...

MY *EYES*-- CAN'T --!

I'LL *KILL* YOU FOR THAT!

UUNNHH!

BLAM

MISERABLE *SCUM*--

IF THAT GIRL IS *DEAD*, I'LL TEAR YOU TO *PIECES!*

OKAY, LITTLE MAN, THAT *DOES* IT! BARE *HANDS* DON'T MEAN *NOTHIN'* TO *"DEVIL" DEVLIN*...

...BUT MY BEAR *HUG* IS GONNA MEAN *PLENTY* TO YOU!

HE'S CRUSHING MY *RIBS*...

...CAN'T *BREATHE...*

...BLACKING OUT...

FOR A TIME, HARRY VINCENT'S MIND WHIRLS IN *DARKNESS*... THEN *CONSCIOUSNESS* CLAWS AT HIS EYELIDS... AND HE OPENS THEM TO FIND...

WELCOME BACK TO THE WORLD OF THE *LIVING*, MR. VINCENT! MY LAND, YOU WERE *OUT* FOR SUCH A *LONG* TIME...

...I WAS BECOMING AFRAID YOU'D *NEVER* WAKE UP! AND *YOU*, MISS... HOW FORTUNATE DEVLIN'S BULLET ONLY *GRAZED* YOU!

FORTUNATE, BLISS ...FOR *WHO?* WHAT DO YOU *WANT* WITH US? JUST WHAT *IS* YOUR RACKET, ANYWAY?

A *RACKET?* MY LAND, *NO*, MR. VINCENT! NOT A RACKET... BUT A *BUSINESS*...

...THE BUSINESS OF... *RESURRECTION!*

YOU SEE, MR. VINCENT, FOR A PRICE, I CAN ARRANGE THE *"DEATH"* OF ANY UNDERWORLD FIGURE WHO WISHES TO... *RETIRE*, SHALL WE SAY?

AN UNRECOGNIZABLE *CORPSE* THAT MATCHES MY CLIENT'S PHYSICAL PROPORTIONS IS PROVIDED BY ONE OF THE COUNTLESS *DERELICTS* FROM MY SALVATION CENTER...

...THEN, ONCE MY CLIENT IS OFFICIALLY DEAD AND BURIED, A NEW *FACE* AND NEW *IDENTIFICATION* ALLOW HIM TO RETURN TO THE WORLD AT LARGE A *NEW* MAN!

THAT STILL DOESN'T EXPLAIN WHAT YOU'RE PLANNING TO DO WITH *US!*

MY LAND, MISS... YOU'RE QUITE *RIGHT!* YOU SEE, MY LATEST CLIENT IS *GUNNER MILLIGAN!* HE AND HIS LADYFRIEND ARE SCHEDULED TO *"DIE"* IN A FLAMING AUTO WRECK...

...AND MOST COINCIDENTALLY, YOU AND MR. VINCENT *MATCH* THEIR PHYSICAL REQUIREMENTS ALMOST *EXACTLY!*

86

HAHAHAHAHA

YES, MURDERER... THE *SHADOW* HAS COME TO MAKE YOU *PAY* FOR YOUR CRIMES...

...AND HE HASN'T COME *ALONE!*

IN MEMORY OF AGNES BLISS

MR. VINCENT... AND THE *GIRL....!*

BUT IT'S NOT *POSSIBLE!* YOU'RE BOTH *DEAD!* I *SAW* YOU DIE!

YOU SAW THE *STATION WAGON* GO OVER A CLIFF, PALLY...NOT *US!*

I *STOPPED* THE CAR SECONDS BEFORE IT REACHED THE CLIFF'S EDGE... *FREED* HARRY AND MARGO...

...THEN ALLOWED THE EMPTY VEHICLE TO *COMPLETE* ITS SUICIDE PLUNGE TO MAKE YOU THINK YOUR PLAN HAD *SUCCEEDED!*

IT CAN *STILL* SUCCEED, SHADOW ...ONCE I BUMP *YOU* OFF!

BLAM

FOOL!

M-MY *GUN*... I'M *FINISHED!*

SPANG

BELIEVE IT, BUSTER... BUT *I'M* GONNA DO THE FINISHING--NOT THE *SHADOW!*

I *OWE* YOU ONE FROM EARLIER THIS EVENING, UGLY! MY BONES *STILL* CREAK FROM THAT *HUG* YOU GAVE ME!

THE NIGHT AIR GROWS *TENSE* AS THE TWO ANTAGONISTS SQUARE OFF FOR *BATTLE...*

A BATTLE DEFINITELY *POST-PONED...* AS HOMER BLISS SEIZES A CHANCE FOR *FREEDOM...*

ALL RIGHT, EVERYBODY... *FREEZE!*

SHADOW, DROP YOUR *WEAPONS...* OR FORCE ME TO *SEVER* THE YOUNG LADY'S *JUGULAR!*

IT APPEARS I HAVE NO *CHOICE!*

CLAT CLAK

YOU *NEVER* HAD A CHOICE, SHADOW!

NOW PLEASE... DON'T ATTEMPT TO *FOLLOW* US... OR, MARK ME, THE GIRL WILL *REGRET* IT!

THEN, AFTER THE FAT MAN AND HIS CAPTIVE HAVE FADED INTO THE DARK...

YUH KNOW SOMETHIN'? YOU BLOODHOUNDS AIN'T GONNA FOLLOW *NOBODY-- NEVER!* FIRST I'LL PLUG VINCENT, THEN *YOU,* BRIGHTEYES...

FOR A SINGLE INSTANT, THE KILLER'S EYES LEAVE THE SHADOW...

...A SINGLE INSTANT *TOO LONG*--

HUNH--? WHERE'D HE *GO?*

BEHIND YOU, KILLER!

BL**AM**

HUH-WAHH!

UH-UH--

HA HA HA HA HA HA

WHILE AT THE WATER'S EDGE...

YOU'RE *UNHARMED,* MARGO?

YES... *FINE*... BUT BLISS IS IN THE *SEA-PLANE*... *ESCAPING*...!

WE'VE *FAILED!*

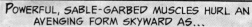

POWERFUL, SABLE-GARBED MUSCLES HURL AN AVENGING FORM SKYWARD AS...

THE SHADOW *NEVER* FAILS!

YOU! YOU RUINED *EVERYTHING!* I WOULD HAVE BEEN *RICH* IF YOU HADN'T INTERFERED!

YOU DESTROYED MY *LIFE'S WORK*... MY *DREAMS*...!

NOW I'LL DESTROY *YOU!*

YOU WILL *TRY,* HOMER BLISS...

...BUT YOU ARE *DOOMED* BEFORE YOU START!

THE WEED OF CRIME BEARS *BITTER* FRUIT, HOMER BLISS!

EEEEYYAA

CRIME DOES NOT *PAY!*

WHUMP

"THE SHADOW *KNOWS!*"

HA HA HA HA HA

From the Shadow's Private Files

The Shadow

CHINATOWN...

IT IS ONE OF THOSE WINTER NIGHTS WHEN THE SKY FALLS LIKE A SHROUD TO COVER THE SLEEPING CITY... TENDRILS OF FOG COLD AS SKELETON'S FINGERS TOUCH ALL AND THERE IS A MUFFLED STILLNESS BROKEN ONLY BY DISTANT MOANS... BODING OF *EVIL* GRIPS MANHATTAN THIS CHILL HOUR...

THE WINDING STREET IS *DESERTED* EXCEPT FOR A HUSKY MAN WITH THE MARK OF *VIOLENCE* ON HIS FACE AND A DEADLY *WEAPON* CRADLED IN HIS ARMS, STANDING AS A *SENTRY* IN FRONT OF A DIMLY LIT DOORWAY, UNAWARE OF THE FIGURE MATERIALIZING FROM THE MISTS OF THE SHADOWS...

NIGHT OF THE NINJA

92

GHHH

HA HA HA HA HA HA

HEY, *BOSS!* WAIT A *MINNIT!*

YOU WERE TOLD TO *KEEP WATCH,* SHREVVY--

--WHY DO YOU *DISOBEY?*

OUR MAN AT *POLICE HEADQUARTERS* JUST DELIVERED A *MESSAGE!* A *RAIDING PARTY'S* ON THE WAY HERE! I FIGURED YOU'D WANNA KNOW BEFORE YOU GO CHARGING INSIDE!

YOU MIGHT BE *TRAPPED!*

I MIGHT *INDEED!* YOU'VE DONE *WELL* TO TELL ME, SHREVVY! I'LL LET THE *LAW* HANDLE THE MCMASTER MOB!

WE'LL *WAIT* AND SNARE ANY WHO *ESCAPE* THE RAIDERS!

THEN-- A *SCREAM* SHRILLS INTO THE AIR...

AAAGHH!

IT SOUNDS AS THOUGH THE POLICE MAY BE *TOO LATE!*

TIE THE *GUARD* I KNOCKED OUT AND AWAIT FURTHER INSTRUCTIONS!

AT THAT INSTANT, ON THE **SECOND FLOOR** OF THE RAMSHACKLE BUILDING, IN A ROOM THICK WITH THE SICKLY SWEET SMELL OF **DRUGS** ...

AL....AM I **SEEIN'** HIM....OR IS THE STUFF WE BEEN SMOKIN' WARPED MY **BRAIN**?

H-HE'S **THERE** --

--AN' HE'S KILLED **MANNY**!

MY MITTS ARE LIKE **SAUSAGES**... CAN'T GET MY **GAT**!

YOU WON'T **NEED** IT--

--IN **HELL**!

UGGHH

TZING

P-PLEASE, MISTER... HAVE **MERCY**!

HAVE **YOU** EVER HAD MERCY ON YOUR VICTIMS? --**NO**!

94

BUT BEFORE THE BLADE CAN DESCEND, AN *AUTOMATIC* SPITS--

HAHA HA H

PANG

HE'S *CRAZY!* DON'T LET 'IM GET *AWAY!*

I DON'T *INTEND* TO!

HE'S LOCKED THE DOOR FROM THE *OTHER SIDE!* I'M *SLOWED* --

KRAK

FWINNG

--BUT NOT *STOPPED!*

FATHER... *FATHER...*

MISS--A MAN RAN THROUGH HERE! WHERE DID HE *GO?*

ONTO THE *ROOF!* HE STABBED MY FATHER AND WENT TO THE *ROOF!*

HE'LL GO NO *FURTHER!*

M-MONEY... WANTS THE MONEY...

FATHER!

HOWEVER, THE CLOAKED AVENGER FINDS THE ROOF *EMPTY!* FOR A HALF MINUTE HE STANDS, SURVEYING THE SCENE...

SUDDENLY, A BRIGHT BEAM OF *LIGHT* STABS AT HIM, AND...

BETTER SURRENDER, FELLA--

--WE GOT THE JOINT SURROUNDED!

SEND A COUPLE OF THE BOYS UP THERE! NOT THAT THERE'S ANY *HURRY*...

...HE'S GOT NO PLACE TO *RUN* TO!

WHIRLING, THE SHADOW RACES ACROSS THE TAR--

96

CALMLY, HE PEERS AT AN ALLEY FULLY *SIXTY FEET* BELOW--

--AND *DROPS!*

IRON FINGERS CLAMP ONTO A *WINDOW SILL*--

--AND A LITHE BODY SWINGS *UPWARD* TO A DOUBTFUL *SAFETY!*

MAN, WE'RE GONNA BE *PROMOTED* FOR SURE! HELPIN' NAB THE *McMASTER GANG*--

--TO SAY NOTHIN' OF THAT *SHADOW* GUY! WE GOT 'IM *CORNERED!*

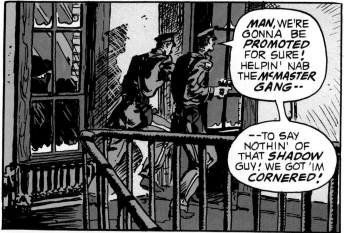

WITHIN *MINUTES...*

WHERE *TO*, BOSS?

CIRCLE THE *BLOCK*, SHREVVY!

THE *SHADOW'S* WORK IS TEMPORARILY *DONE!*

BUT *LAMONT CRANSTON* IS *CURIOUS!*

A QUICK CHANGE OF CLOTHING AND A SHORT DRIVE, AND...

LOOK, SHREWY-- MY FRIEND G. OYLE PROUD!

I SAY THIS CITY HAS BECOME A *CESSPOOL* OF LAWLESSNESS AND I MEAN TO *DO* SOMETHING ABOUT IT!

--SURROUNDED BY REPORTERS... AS *USUAL,* EH, PROUD?

AH...*LAMONT CRANSTON!* I WAS JUST TELLING THESE CHAPS WHAT I PROPOSE TO DO WHEN I'M ELECTED *DISTRICT ATTORNEY!*

GANGSTERS GOING TO *DOPE DENS* LIKE THE ONE IN THAT BUILDING... VIGILANTES LIKE THE *SHADOW...* *INTOLERABLE!*

MY FIRST STEP WILL BE TO *ELIMINATE* THE DRUG TRAFFIC! I'VE RECENTLY RETURNED FROM A TRIP TO THE *FAR EAST--*

--WHERE THE DRUGS *COME FROM!* I'VE INVESTIGATED... AND I HAVE A PLAN FOR CHOKING *OFF* THIS INSIDIOUS ACTIVITY!

YOU'LL *TALK* IT TO DEATH, MR. PROUD?

AH...MY ERSTWHILE *OPPONENT* IN THE FORTHCOMING ELECTION-- *BARTLETT MOGEN...* THE *PRESENT* DISTRICT ATTORNEY!

A MAN WHO HAS *DISGRACED* THE OFFICE HE NOW HOLDS BY HIS *SOFT* ATTITUDE TO CRIME!

MY *ATTITUDE* MAY BE SOFT--

--BUT NOT MY *HEAD...* WHICH IS MORE THAN I CAN SAY FOR CERTAIN YOUNG *REFORMERS!*

IF YOU GENTLEMEN OF THE PRESS CARE TO JOIN ME, WE'LL WET THE WHISTLE AND DISCUSS THE *YANKEES'* CHANCES TO WIN THE PENNANT!

THERE GOES EVERYTHING THAT'S *WRONG* WITH OUR CITY, LAMONT *!* HE'S *OLD, LAZY*... AND *CORRUPT !*

COULD *BE*, OLD CHAP! WHAT SAY WE DISCUSS IT *TOMORROW* AT THE CLUB? I'M *FRIGHTFULLY* TIRED --

--I'VE BEEN UP SINCE *NOON !*

SLEEP *TIGHT,* LAMONT *!*

YA *REALLY* GONNA CATCH SOME SHUT-EYE, BOSS ?

OF *COURSE* NOT, SHREVVY! -- TO *HEADQUARTERS !*

ARRIVING AT A SUITE SOME-WHERE IN THE HEART OF NEW YORK, THE SHADOW QUICKLY RELATES THE EVENING'S EVENTS TO HIS LOYAL *TEAM*--

JUDGING FROM HIS *COSTUME* AND *WEAPONS*, I'D SAY THE KILLER I MET IS A *NINJA !*

WEREN'T THEY *SPIES* IN ANCIENT *JAPAN?*

YES... *EXTREMELY* SKILLED IN *STEALTH* AND *ASSASSINATION!* RIGHT, SHADOW ?

ANYONE FAMILIAR WITH THOSE ARTS COULD BE A *FORMIDABLE* OPPONENT !

PRECISELY, MARGO! I *STUDIED* WITH A NINJA MASTER YEARS AGO! I LEARNED *MUCH* FROM HIM !

THEREFORE... *ATTENTION* TO ORDERS !

BURBANK...TELEPHONE OUR UNDERWORLD CONTACTS! WE'LL PAY *HANDSOMELY* FOR ANY PERTINENT INFORMATION!

MARGO ... YOU'LL QUESTION THE CHINESE GIRL WHOSE FATHER WAS SLAIN IN THE MORNING!

HARRY... YOU'LL STAND BY!

OKAY...BUT YOU'RE MAKING A CERTAIN *MISS* MIGHTY UNHAPPY! I PROMISED THE DAY TO *HER*!

SHE'LL *LIVE*, TIGER!

HEY, CHIEF! ONE THING'S *BOTHERING* ME! WHY ARE WE TRYING TO *NAIL* THIS *NINJA*? YOU SAID HE SMASHED THE MCMASTER CREW...JUST LIKE *YOU* WERE GOING TO!

SOUNDS LIKE HE'S ON *OUR* SIDE!

MY *INSTINCT* SAYS HE *ISN'T*, HARRY! DO YOU CARE TO *QUARREL* WITH MY INSTINCT?

LEAVE ME NOW! I MUST *THINK*!

AT EXACTLY *TWELVE* THE FOLLOWING DAY, LAMONT CRANSTON ARRIVES AT THE EXCLUSIVE *COBALT CLUB* AND GREETS --

PROUD, OLD CHAP! OUT FOR A *WALK*? I'LL *JOIN* YOU!

I'VE BEEN MEANING TO GIVE YOU THIS *CHECK--* A *CAMPAIGN* CONTRIBUTION!

ACCEPTED WITH *GRATITUDE,* CRANSTON!

AT THAT INSTANT, FROM THE CORNER OF HIS EYE, THE DISGUISED AVENGER SEES SOMETHING *GLEAMING ... SPINNING--*

--AND HE *REACTS!*

SORRY, PROUD--!

DON'T BE, CRANSTON! I BELIEVE YOU SAVED MY *LIFE!* IF YOU HADN'T *JOSTLED* ME...

...THIS THING WOULD HAVE BURIED ITSELF IN MY *WINDPIPE!*

IT'S A *NINJA STAR...* *NASTY* DEVICE!

NO *POSSIBILITY* OF TELLING WHO *THREW* IT! --NOT WITH THE STREET SO *MOBBED!*

EXACTLY, CRANSTON! IT COULD HAVE COME FROM *ANYWHERE!*

PROUD, DO ME A *FAVOR!* LET ME PUT YOU UNDER THE PROTECTION OF A FRIEND OF MINE... *HARRY VINCENT!*

YOU'RE TOO *VALUABLE* A MAN TO LOSE TO A *KILLER!*

I DON'T NEED A *NURSEMAID...*

I WON'T TAKE *NO* FOR AN ANSWER!

AN HOUR LATER, IN *CHINATOWN --*

MISS... *MISS!*

YOU SPEAK TO *ME?*

YES...I'D LIKE TO ASK YOU A FEW *QUESTIONS!*

PLEASE TO STEP *INSIDE--!*

IT'S SO *DARK* IN HERE!

YOU WILL NOT *NEED* TO SEE!

UNNGH!

YOU *STRUCK* HER *BRUTALLY!* *

SHE MEANT YOU NO *HARM!*

PERHAPS *NOT*, MY BROTHERS--

*NOTE: THIS DIALOGUE TRANSLATED FROM THE CHINESE!

--BUT I CANNOT TAKE THE *CHANCE*... NOT WHEN WE ARE NEAR TO *ACCOMPLISHING* OUR MISSION!

GUARD HER-- AND THE *MONEY!*

I AM *TROUBLED*, SISTER! THE MONEY-- IT IS NOT *OURS!* IT IS *DIRTY* MONEY... MADE FROM TRADING IN ILLEGAL *DRUGS!*

OUR FATHER *REALIZED* THAT, MY BROTHER--

--BUT WITHOUT IT, WE COULD NOT BRING OUR *RELATIVES* TO THIS COUNTRY!

THAT IS WHY OUR FATHER TOOK IT FROM... *HIM!*

I HAVE A *TASK!* WAIT FOR ME!

A DISTANT RUMBLE OF *THUNDER* HERALDS NIGHT, AND FLASHES OF LIGHTNING BLAZE BRIEFLY IN THE RAPIDLY DARKENING SKY!

WET BREEZES WHISTLE THROUGH THE CITY'S CANYONS AND RATTLE THE WINDOWS IN THIS MIDTOWN *APARTMENT* BUILDING...

...AND, *INSIDE*--

BLOWING UP A *MEAN* ONE OUT THERE, MR. PROUD!

I *WISH* YOU'D GO HOME, MR. VINCENT! I'M *PERFECTLY* SAFE!

YEAH, WELL... I'LL STICK AROUND *ANYWAY!*

YOU'RE AS STUBBORN AS *CRANSTON!*

HERE... YOU MAY AS WELL HAVE A CUP OF *COFFEE!*

I'LL BE IN MY STUDY, PREPARING A *CAMPAIGN* SPEECH!

GIVE 'EM *HECK,* MR. PROUD!

AGGH... *ODD* TASTE! --BITTER!

...FEEL *FUNNY*... DIZZY!

PROUD!-- PROUD! I'M SICK--

YOU! THE *NINJA*... GONNA BLOW YOU *AWAY*... IF I CAN RAISE MY *GUN*...

SLPP

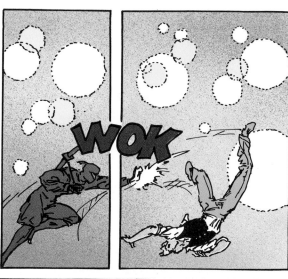
WOK

THROBBING, *AGONIZING* MINUTES PASS, AND THEN...

P-PROUD! YOU *HERE*?

GONE! ...LOOKS LIKE HE PUT UP A *FIGHT,* THOUGH!

I KEEP BLANKIN' *OUT*... GOTTA CALL *HEADQUARTERS* BEFORE I SLEEP *PERMANENTLY!*

HELLO, BURBANK! LISTEN QUICK...THE *NINJA'S* TAKEN *PROUD* AND I'M *USELESS*... BEEN FED SOME SORT OF *POISON!*

I'LL NOTIFY THE *SHADOW* AND SEND AN AMBULANCE FOR YOU!

AT *NINE,* THE STORM FINALLY BREAKS! THE STREETS OF CHINATOWN ARE ABRUPTLY *DESERTED* AS THE GOOD CITIZENS SCURRY FOR *SHELTER*...

105

YOU DIDN'T REPORT AS I *DIRECTED!* AND YOU ARE A LOYAL *AGENT!* THEREFORE, YOU HAD TO BE IN *DANGER!*

AND YOU CAME *A-CHARGING!* AT LEAST I CAN'T SAY YOU *NEGLECT* ME--EXACTLY!

SHADOW...SHE'S *THROWING SOMETHING!*

YES...AS SHE THREW A *SIMILAR* OBJECT AT *PROUD--*

CHING

--A *NINJA STAR!*

THEN *SHE'S* THE NINJA?

NO! SHE IS SMALL...SHE WOULDN'T HAVE THE *STRENGTH* TO DRIVE A *BROKEN SWORD* INTO HER FATHER!

AND SHE HAD NO *MOTIVE* TO KILL HIM! SHE *HAD* THE MONEY!

I HAD IT... AND *HE* WANTED IT-- *ALL!* HE WOULD NOT BE CONTENT WITH A *SHARE,* AS HE AND MY FATHER AGREED!

I SOUGHT TO AVENGE MY FATHER--

--AND TO FINISH MY FATHER'S *WORK* OF FREEING OUR PEOPLE...

GHAAH!

108

SHE'S *DEAD!* SOMEONE AT THE *WINDOW* THREW A... WHAT *IS* IT, SHADOW?

A *NINJA* SPIKE, MARGO! A DEVICE WITH *TWO* USES! IT CAN BE EMPLOYED AS A *WEAPON*--

--OR A *PAIR* OF THESE CAN BE USED FOR *CLIMBING*--LIKE MOUNTAINEERS' *PITONS!*

THAT IS HOW THE NINJA ELUDED ME ON THE *ROOF*...WHILE I WAS BUSY EVADING THE *POLICE*, HE WENT DOWN THE FAR WALL!

YOU SOUND AS THOUGH YOU KNOW HIS *IDENTITY!*

I *DO*, MARGO! I GO TO DELIVER HIS FILTHY *LOOT* TO HIM--IN *PERSON!*

I DO NOT THINK HE WILL BE HAPPY TO *SEE* ME!

NOW, THE STORM *RAGES* LIKE A LIVING BEING... CRYING, CRYING FOR *VENGEANCE!*

IN THIS FAMILIAR BUILDING, LIGHTS DIM, FLICKER...

110

The stories you have just read were originally
published some fifteen years ago . . . but the passage
of time has not diluted Michael Wm. Kaluta's
love for The Shadow.

In the following piece, written and illustrated by
Kaluta and colored by Elaine Lee especially for
this volume, Kaluta once more adds to the legend
of The Shadow with the tale of a kidnapped
child—and the machinations of the Chinese
mastermind known as Wing Fat . . .

GOOD EVENING, LISTENERS. I'M STANDING IN A CROWD OF CURIOUS ONLOOKERS AND A HOST OF POLICE OFFICERS, ALL STARING AT THE HORRIFIC SCENE BEFORE US.

HOW CAN I PICTURE THIS FOR YOU...

THE ONCE-BEAUTIFUL OAK DOORS ARE BURST IN...

...THE ATTRACTIVE FURNITURE STREWN ABOUT THE APARTMENT...

...CURTAINS ARE PULLED DOWN...

...WINDOWS BROKEN.

THERE ARE TWO, PERHAPS THREE HUMAN FORMS THROWN IN THE CORNER LIKE RAG DOLLS.

LISTENERS, YOU'VE JUST HEARD POLICE COMMISSIONER WESTON TELL US THAT THE YOUNG SON OF THE VISITING JAPANESE AMBASSADOR HAS BEEN ABDUCTED, HIS GUARDS AND FAMILY RETAINERS MURDERED HERE IN THIS EXCLUSIVE HOTEL APARTMENT HIGH ABOVE THE STREETS OF MANHATTAN.

A SHROUD OF MYSTERY HANGS OVER THIS SAD EVENT.

SOMEWHERE IN THIS CITY IS A CHILD...

...TERRIFIED...

...IN WHO KNOWS WHAT PERIL...

...HIS FAMILY RETAINERS BUTCHERED BEFORE HIS YOUNG EYES.

WHAT OTHER SCENES OF DEPRAVITY MUST HE BE WITNESSING?

WHAT UNKNOWN TORTURES MUST HE EVEN NOW BE FACING?

WE RETURN YOU NOW TO OUR REGULARLY SCHEDULED BROADCAST...

BLAM!

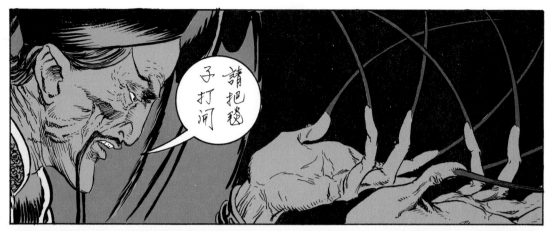

126

My thanks to Will Murray and Anthony Tollin for their help in keeping my facts straight.

—DENNIS O'NEIL

To Denny O'Neil, for putting up with me.

—MIKE KALUTA